First Words
with
Peppa Pig™
Level 2

Grandad Dog's Garage

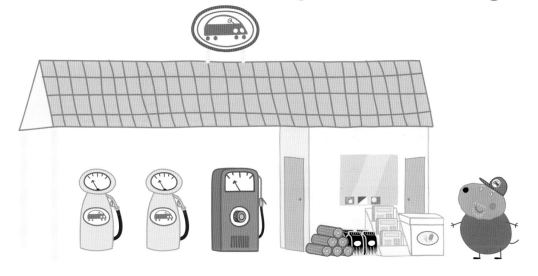

Based on the Peppa Pig TV series

Meet

Peppa   George   Suzy Sheep

Mummy Pig   Daddy Pig   Grandpa Pig   Grandad Dog

Learn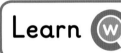

came   get   must   no   now

on   our   out   please   ran

ride   too   went   with   yes

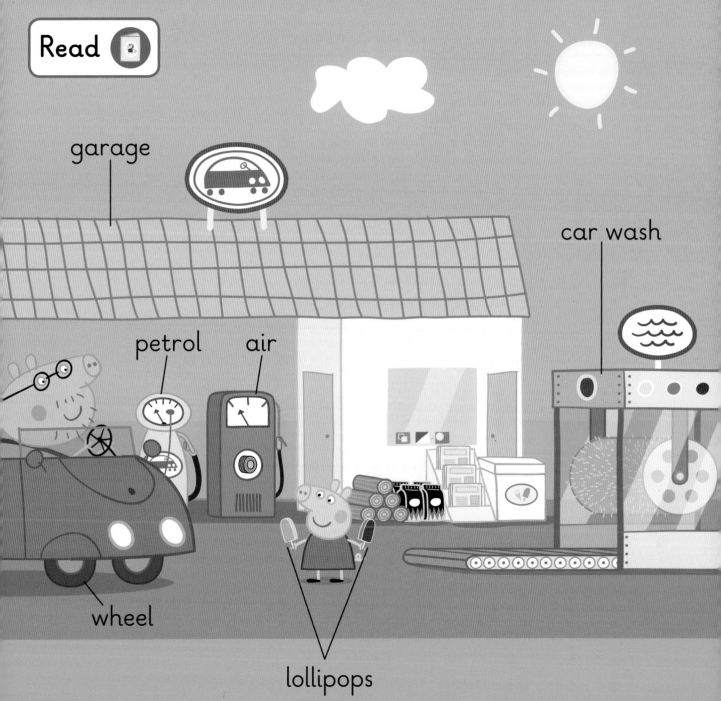

garage

car wash

petrol

air

wheel

lollipops

3

This is Grandad Dog's garage.

Cars go to the garage to get petrol, so they do not run out. They get air for the wheels and go in the car wash, too.

Peppa went on a big car ride with Daddy Pig, Mummy Pig and George. "We must go to Grandad Dog's garage now," said Daddy Pig.

"Do you need air?" said Grandad Dog.
"No, thank you. Our wheels have lots of air,"
said Daddy Pig.

"Can we get two lollipops, please?" said Daddy Pig.
"Yes," said Grandad Dog. "Do you need to get
petrol for the big car ride, too?"

"No," said Daddy Pig. "We have lots of petrol for our big car ride."

Peppa went on the big car ride with
Daddy Pig, Mummy Pig and George.
The car ran out of petrol.
It came to a stop.

"We did not have lots of petrol," said Peppa.
"No," said Daddy Pig. "We ran out."
"We must call Grandad Dog now," said Peppa.
"Yes, we must," said Daddy Pig.

Grandad Dog came to find the car.
"The car ran out of petrol?" said Grandad Dog.

"Yes, our car ran out of petrol," said Daddy Pig.
"You must ride to the garage with me,"
said Grandad Dog.
"Yes, please!" said Peppa.

Peppa went on a ride with Grandad Dog.

George, Mummy Pig and Daddy Pig went, too.
It was fun!

The car came to Grandad Dog's garage.
"Can you fill the car with petrol, please?"
said Daddy Pig.

Grandad Dog filled the car with petrol.
"Now, the car will go," he said.

Suzy Sheep's car had a flat wheel.
The air had run out.
"I must go and help Suzy Sheep," said Grandad Dog.

"Can I please ride in the truck with Grandad Dog?" said Peppa.
"Yes," said Daddy Pig.

Grandad Dog came to find the car.
"Can you fill the wheel with petrol, please?"
said Suzy Sheep.

"No, but I can fill the wheel with air!"
said Grandad Dog.
"Not too much!" said Suzy Sheep.
"Now, the car will go," said Grandad Dog.

A new car came to
Grandad Dog's garage.
"Have you run out of petrol and
air, too?" said Grandad Dog.

"No, our car went in the mud." said Grandpa Pig.
"Now, our car must go in the car wash, please!"

"You can all come to my garage for help!"
said Grandad Dog.